love in the dark

a his and hers activity book

with glow-in-the-dark features

Juliette Wills has been a journalist for 10 years, specialising in sport, music and sex because, she says, 'Nothing else matters'. Juliette wrote a regular sex column for *Loaded* magazine, features about sex for various women's magazines including *Marie Claire* and interviewed sexy pop stars for the likes of *Q* and *The Guardian*. She is also responsible for setting up David and Victoria Beckham through an interview she did with The Spice Girls, and claims that playing cupid to the world's sexiest couple and wearing stilettos and leopard print underwear to clean the bathroom qualifies her to pass on her wisdom to the rest of us.

Copyright © 2004 Quid Publishing Ltd

Published by HarperCollins*Entertainment*
77–85 Fulham Palace Road
London W6 8JB

www.harpercollins.co.uk

ISBN 0-00-717786-0

Conceived, designed and produced by
Quid Publishing Ltd
Fourth Floor
Sheridan House
112 Western Road
Hove BN3 1DD

www.quidpublishing.com

Publisher: Nigel Browning
Design: Lindsey Johns
Project Management: JMS Books LLP
Illustrations: Matt Pagett
Initial Concept Credit: Stephen Melhuish

Printed and Bound in Hong Kong by Regent Publishing Services, Ltd

love in the dark

a his and **hers** activity book
with glow-in-the-dark features

Juliette Wills

HarperCollins*Entertainment*
An Imprint of HarperCollins*Publishers*

How Sexy Are You?

You don't have to look like a movie star or a supermodel to be sexy, although admittedly, it does help. Being sexy is all about the individual and how sexy you are to that special someone. While one man might find the fact that you can drink him under the table rather threatening, not to say expensive, another might view a good head for drink as an attribute that renders you deeply attractive. While huge boobs may be one guy's thing, another might run a mile if Pamela Anderson so much as even pointed her nipples in his direction. So, one person's definition of what is sexy is not necessarily another's. But there are some looks that will mark you out as just about sexy as a Victorian bathing suit and others that will have him needing to put out a small fire in his underpants.

Think of famous women who you consider sexy and then think of women you know, or have seen in the street or in magazines, who you thought had the 'it' factor. What was it about them? Was it their clothes, their attitude, the way they carried themselves? Being sexy isn't something which you should have to work at, it's something which comes naturally.

Wearing a man's shirt around the house can look really sexy (not with tracksuit bottoms and your granny's slippers) and so can tucking into a great big steak instead of chasing a salad around your plate. Sometimes the weirdest habits are the sexiest for him, such as the way you push your hair back over your ear or even the way you shower.

 "When I'm good I'm very, very good... but when I'm bad I'm better"

Original sex siren and Hollywood goddess Mae West

Do you put the 'sex' into sexy?

When dressing for a dinner date with a new man, which outfit do you choose?:

a) A low-cut top, mini skirt, stockings, suspenders and sky-high stilettos.
b) A smart trouser suit with a pretty camisole top underneath and kitten heels.
c) Jeans and whatever T-shirt happens to be on top of the heap on the floor.

When you want to make the first move, what do you do?

a) Put your hand on his crotch and whisper, 'Take me, now big boy'.
b) Put your fingers to his lips to stop him talking and then lean in slowly for a kiss.
c) Not bother. After all, it's up to him, isn't it?

Your idea of a blowjob is:

a) Anytime, anywhere, even if you're both in the supermarket.
b) A bit of a treat, so I take my time and enjoy it as much as he does.
c) Hard work – that's why they call it a job, isn't it?

When discussing fantasies, you're likely to respond by saying:

a) 'I want you, your brother, your best mate and your Dad, now.'
b) 'A weekend in a log cabin, just you and me and a big furry rug.'
c) 'I'd really love it if you'd clean the bathroom and make me a cup of tea.'

conclusion So, are you about as sexy as an old oven glove or have you got 'it' big time, without even knowing it?

Mostly a's: Take it easy – either you've been watching too many dodgy films or you've got a hormone imbalance. Remember, less is more! **Mostly b's:** He's a very lucky man – could you possibly be any sexier? You've got it down to a fine art, give a little, but not all **Mostly c's:** Hello? What are you, his mother? Give the man a break and sort yourself out, before even the postman stops calling.

The Etiquette Of Seduction

There are certain signs that will tell you whether you're in with a chance with a man. Since women are generally rather better at communicating than men, you'll soon have a good idea if he's interested or not. This will avoid embarrassing situations, such as his wife asking you to climb down from his lap so that she can take him home. But there are also less obvious signs indicating that a man is off limits or, on the contrary, that he is positively salivating at the very thought of touching even your knees. Ask him about himself – men love nothing better than to talk about Number One. If you really like him, try your best to stay awake when he does, even if he mentions cricket or steam trains. Although on second thoughts, maybe that would be a good time to leave.

Here's how to work it all out:

Top Tip: men need your intentions to be obvious. Stroke your neck, run your fingers through your hair, hitch up your skirt or bend down to pick something up and give him a flash of your fancy knickers – anything to draw attention to your body, short of actually throwing yourself at him as if he were on fire.

◀ *He's looking at you kid – the intense gaze and tilted angle of his head are sure signs that he's up for it*

Good Signs

1 When you smile at him, he smiles back and holds your gaze for a few seconds longer than he should.

2 If you approach him when he's with friends, he breaks away from the group to talk to you, despite loud teasing and shouts of 'Go on my son!' or those stupid 'Wey-hey!' sounds that men make when they are unable to form a proper sentence.

3 When you talk to him, he leans forward, brushes your hair away from your face and touches your arm, or looks into your eyes and actually appears to be listening to what you're saying.

4 If you mention going out for a drink or for dinner, his eyes light up and he gives you his card. He then asks for your number and suggests a firm date, rather than just saying 'I'll call you some time.'

5 He compliments you on your clothes, your perfume or even your elbows and blushes if you pay him a compliment.

Bad Signs

1 When you smile at him he grimaces or heads for the door.

2 If you approach him when he's with friends, he backs off, hides behind them or whispers something that makes them all snigger. If they then say, 'He fancies your mate' or if he tells you he is married/gay/suffering from a terminal disease with less than two months to live, certainly not long enough to go on a date with you, then things don't look too good.

3 When you talk to him, he leans back, yawns, looks around the room orbecomes fascinated by the logo on his beer mat. He falls asleep while you are talking.

4 If you mention going out for a drink or for dinner, his face contorts, he looks to the heavens for inspiration and comes up with, 'I can't, I need to shampoo my dog' or 'I'd love to but I don't eat.'

5 He tells you his mum has the same dress as the one you're wearing, or worse, his ex-girlfriend looks like you and was 'a total bitch'. It's time to head for the door.

Foreplanning For Foreplay

Ok, you've done the hard bit. He's interested, so all you have to do now is keep him that way. In the early days of a relationship certain things may frighten a man off and that doesn't just mean an angry husband, large dog or oddball flatmate. As a rule, a woman's place is tidier and cleaner than a man's. However, rules are made to be broken and it has been known for some women to live in such a state of disarray that they are unable to find the kitchen beneath the mess, let alone the door keys. Hiding all traces of your past, present and future is taking things a little far, but do have the sense to lock away those few items that could have him running for the door faster than you can say, 'But what about your coffee/toast/cup of Nippy Noodles?'

Up there with the worst things that can greet a man as he steps over the threshold of your home is the sight of your beloved (to you) cat. He may not dislike cats per se, but some men have a built-in radar system that is able to sense when a cat means more to its owner than he is ever likely to, and generally, that's just about all the time. Cats are possessive little creatures. They may rub up against your leg in an endearing way, but they also know just how to rub a man up the wrong way, making him feel about as desirable as something you might find in their litter tray. Acknowledge your pet when you walk in, feed it if you must, but don't pick it up and start talking in the voice of a demented child about how gorgeous it is and how much it will like 'Mummy's new boyfriend'. If you want the latter to run for

the hills, go ahead and do just that.

Books are another thing. Men don't necessarily rifle through things as women sometimes do, but a quick scan of a room will have him making his mind up about you in one minute flat (or less, depending on the size of the room and the nature of the reading matter). Books entitled 'How to Meet a Man', 'How Not to Remain Single' or 'How to Make Him Marry You and Love Your Cat Too' should not feature on your bookshelf in the first place, and if they do, should certainly not be displayed. Hide provocative volumes alongside your cleaning products. Even if he ends up moving in, he will never look there!

The same applies to books on babies' names, any aspect of pregnancy and spells and incantations to snare your ideal man. On the other hand, impressive literature to

▲ *Learn to keep your furry friends locked up when seducing your man – huggable lovelies can be total passion-killers.*

leave lying around includes recipe books, anything with Kylie Minogue on the cover and music magazines, all interesting but harmless enough. But don't leave women's magazines open at articles such as 'Why are all men useless?' or 'Ten easy steps to getting him up the aisle'.

One of the most heinous crimes, however, takes place in the bedroom. Cuddly toys, bears with T-shirts saying 'I Wuv You' or, even worse, 'Wuv Me'

should be banned globally. If you have been given one and have yet to burn it, hide it in your wardrobe. Photos of current or ex–boyfriends in fancy frames by the bed should also take a walk, along with reading glasses with unattractively thick lenses, earplugs, eye masks and anything else that marks you out as old before your time, including bedsocks, hot water bottles and, heaven forbid, dentures.

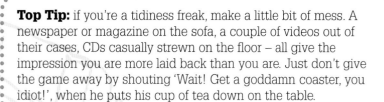

Top Tip: if you're a tidiness freak, make a little bit of mess. A newspaper or magazine on the sofa, a couple of videos out of their cases, CDs casually strewn on the floor – all give the impression you are more laid back than you are. Just don't give the game away by shouting 'Wait! Get a goddamn coaster, you idiot!', when he puts his cup of tea down on the table.

love in the dark

Erogenous Zones

Both men and women have major and minor erogenous zones, and there are different ways of working around them. Licking, stroking, nibbling, sucking and gentle blowing can all have the desired effect; it just takes practice to work out which zone and what kind of pressure or sensation your man enjoys most. Here are a few helpful tips:

Some men are sent into a state of ecstasy when a women blows gently on the back of their neck, but for others it leaves them no more excited than being asked to take out the trash. What turns one man on can turn another off. Don't be afraid to ask if your boyfriend is enjoying what you're doing, or try to read the signs yourself. If he's asleep while you're licking his nipples, you know a new strategy is required.

"Getting what you want from your men is all about knowing how to ask for it"
Snow White

Take her advice – tell him what you like and where you like it

▶▶▶ **The major male erogenous zones are as follows:**

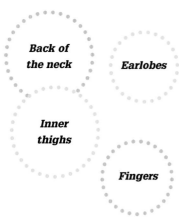

Lips

Nipples

Willy

Perennium (the area between the balls and the anus)

Balls

▶▶▶ **The minor male erogenous zones include the following:**

Back of the neck

Earlobes

Inner thighs

Fingers

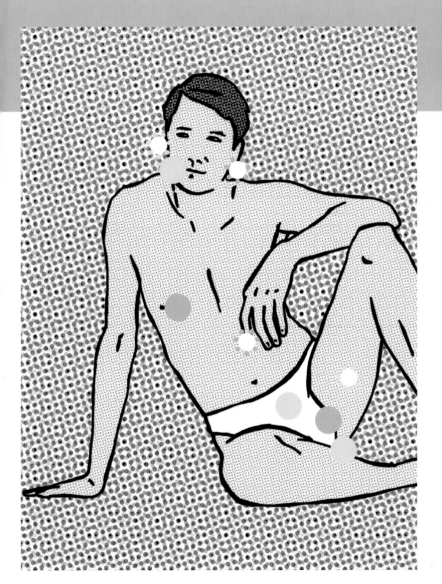

If he's moaning (as in sighing, rather than complaining), then you're on the right track. The same goes with the anus. Some men enjoy a woman probing this zone with a well lubricated finger or tongue, while others hate being touched there and will scream, 'What are you doing, woman? I'm not gay!' whilst throwing you across the room like a hot potato.

Sensual Massage

First things first – if you're using a condom, make sure you avoid mineral-based massage oils, such as baby oil, as they can erode the rubber, rendering them useless for protective purposes. A huge range of oils specifically tailored to sensual massage is widely available in most supermarkets and pharmacies. But if you're looking for something with a particular aroma or if you want to make absolutely sure the oil can be used with condoms (the packaging will specify this), then you might want to visit a specialist sex shop. Alternatively, body lotion or whipped cream will do.

Massage Techniques

Start by asking your boyfriend to lie face down on the bed or floor, naked, arms by his side or elbows by his head, depending on what is most comfortable for him. Sit astride his buttocks or kneel by his side. Pour a small amount of lotion or oil into the palm of your hand to warm it (cold oil on his back won't help him relax) and then smooth it onto his back with your palms, using a circular motion. Start from the small of his back and work outwards in repeated strokes, using the ball of your thumb to apply pressure as you do so. Move upwards towards the neck and shoulders, increasing the pressure as you get higher. When you reach his shoulders, feel for any knots and knead them gently, using your finger tips and the base of your thumbs. Ask him to tell you if the pressure is too hard or too light and keep going for as long as you can. He should be relaxed after around fifteen minutes – any longer and he may fall asleep. If you've got the energy, repeat the same techniques on his buttocks and down his thighs and calves. If he's been playing football, he'll appreciate a good massage on the backs of the legs. Keep rubbing the oil between your hands before applying it and don't be afraid to use a reasonable amount. You don't want him slipping off the bed, but a dry massage is uncomfortable and feels the same as a carpet burn!

Sit on the sofa behind your partner with your legs around him and start massaging him in this position. He can rest his hands on your thighs and you are in prime position to nibble his earlobes, neck and shoulders if you want to take things further more quickly

Top Tip: if you feel he's sufficiently aroused and if you're in the mood, rub some oil into your own thighs and sit astride him. Massage him with your thighs, gently moving up and down while gripping his buttocks between your legs gently. Slide off and ask him to turn over – you'll be greeted with more than a smile...

Sex Foods

Ask any man about his idea of erotic eating and he'll doubtless reply an all-day breakfast or his mother's apple pie. They say that the quickest way to a man's heart is through his stomach, but we all know that isn't true – it's through his willy, and those all-day breakfasts are more likely to be the quickest route to a heart attack. So, rather than try and fill

▶▶▶ Oysters

These are said to resemble a woman's genitals (although being told your vagina resembles a grey, slimy shellfish is a strange form of compliment). The taste, smell and texture of oysters are all extremely sensual, and you might get lucky and find a pearl at the same time, symbolic of the clitoris, of course. Zinc is found in abundance in oysters and is renowned for providing men with potent sperm. Many men lack zinc since, with each ejaculation they kiss goodbye to around a third of their daily zinc requirement.

▶▶▶ Figs

Figs are also thought to look like the female genitalia. When a man licks and sucks a fig he apparently finds it quite a turn-on, as does, no doubt, any woman watching.

love in the dark

14

him up, try and turn him on. Here are a few ideas to get him in the mood. While knocking up a fancy meal is a good way to show off your skills in the kitchen before those in the bedroom, if you're likely to burn everything in sight including your eyebrows then nip to the supermarket instead for some aphrodisiac foods which do all the hard work for you.

▶▶▶ Bananas

Your boyfriend will probably prefer to watch you enjoy this particular fruit. Begin by peeling it as seductively as you can – and very gently, or it may break in half, rub it against your nether regions or nipples until his pupils dilate and he breaks out into a sweat. Then feed it to him, continuing to peel it as you go. Bananas contain magnesium, an essential element in the maintenance of a healthy balance of male sex hormones. Bet you never knew that! Keep peeling!

▶▶▶ Honey

Honey provides essential nutrients for a man's sperm count and fertility. What clever little things bees are and, as a bonus, honey also tastes nice. Choose the runny kind and pour it in a steady line from his chest to his willy and then lick if off. Keep going up his body until you are facing him with a mouthful of honey. Then kiss him deeply, and supply him with those vital nutrients in a much more interesting way than via a simple piece of toast.

More Than Two Players

If you're considering involving a third party in your sex life (and that doesn't mean a relationship counsellor), you should be aware that a threesome takes both planning and preparation. The alternative is to get very drunk and suddenly find yourself in bed with your boyfriend and his best mate, without having the first idea how it happened.

There are many things to consider before you consider it, if that makes sense. Firstly, ask yourself if your relationship is strong enough to involve a third person, even on a one-off basis. How do you think you would feel watching your boyfriend get off with another woman? How would he react if he saw you giving another man a blow job? Emotions could run riot when all you had in mind was a little extra action in the sack, perhaps even culminating in the break-up of your relationship, if either you or your boyfriend became besotted with the third person.

A lot of women fantasise about having sex with two men at the same time, but it's not unheard of for women to fancy sex with their boyfriend and another woman. If this is the case, invariably it is the sex with the other woman that is the more experimental and enjoyable part. So, how would your boyfriend react? Perhaps he will enjoy watching the pair of you, as you would hope. Equally he might sit seething in a corner, wanting to join in but realising that you are quite happy without him just now. Sex with two men can have the same

effect, but unless your boyfriend has a real surprise in store, it's unlikely you'll be watching him have sex with the other guy. If you are, then you're probably in trouble anyway. It's more likely that he won't exactly revel in the fact that you're getting off with another man while he awaits his turn. He probably won't enjoy fiddling with your toes while you dangle your ankles above the other guy's head. And imagine the scenario if you have OK sex with your boyfriend but great, blow-your-mind sex with the other guy.

However, if you do decide to go ahead, don't get too drunk, although it is a good idea to warm things up beforehand with a little champagne all round. The third party should not be someone you've just met at the bar, nor should it be a female friend of yours or your boyfriend. You wouldn't want her to be a constant reminder of the night you realised your boyfriend fancied her more than he fancies you. This would do nothing for your friendship, or your relationship. A good solution is to recruit someone over the Internet via a swingers website.

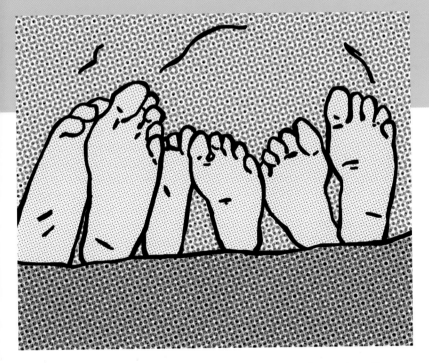

Hopefully, you'll be able to look at a photo and discover a little more about them ('Hi, I'm Andrew and I enjoy light housework and anal penetration'). If he sounds promising agree to meet in advance to check that you fancy him and that your boyfriend doesn't want to punch him on sight. The same applies if the third party is to be a woman, if that is the way you choose to go. Unless she is a total dog, he is likely to say yes. You are the one who will need convincing. The alternative is to try fetish clubs or rely on word of mouth. Handing out flyers asking, 'Anyone fancy a threesome? Our place, Tuesday, 6pm, bring your own bottle' is not advisable. It might be preferable just to talk about what you would like to do and leave it at that. Threesomes are hard work. With all those elbows and feet in the way, it can be like cooking a full English breakfast, blindfolded and on rollerblades.

Top Tip: The best time to try a threesome is when you're single – then nobody gets hurt. All you have to do is find two gorgeous men willing to help you out... and the best place for that is a football club as they'll be used to seeing each other naked after a 90-minute session!

Going Down

The good news is that it is difficult to give a bad blow job. Men are simple creatures, and the very fact that you are even headed in that direction is usually enough to get him excited. Make it a good one and he'll remember you forever. Bear in mind that the idea is not simply to suck on his willy as if it were an ice lolly and just hope for the best. Good technique takes practice, but you can bet he won't mind if you practise on him until you are absolutely perfect.

▲ *The look of lust – make eye-contact when you're down there. It will drive him wild with desire.*

▶▶▶ Use fruit-flavoured condoms during oral sex as a prelude to penetrative sex. Not only do they taste good (strawberry in particular!), but it's a good way to lubricate the condom without resorting to spermicide, which can cause allergic reactions in some women.

Firstly, don't rush it. Take your time getting there – kiss and nibble your way down his neck and shoulders, flick your tongue across his nipples and run your tongue from his belly button round to his inner thigh. Then gently lick his balls. By now he should be begging you to get on with it. Cup his balls with one hand and hold his willy firmly with the other, using your whole hand to encircle it, rather than just your thumb and forefinger. It's not as if you are holding a dainty cup of tea.

Lick your lips to moisten them and then push his willy against your lips without letting him into your mouth. Then, slowly, guide him into your mouth, snaking your tongue from side to side as you work your way down as far as you can without gagging. It may sound weird, but let yourself dribble down him to keep things nice and wet. While you run one hand up and down his willy, flick your tongue gently across the tip and then take him deep into your mouth. Some men enjoy it when you pull their willy down slightly and away from their body, but go easy on this as it's a matter of individual taste (theirs rather than yours). Pushing your tongue against the willy just under the head and then kissing and licking the length of it with

the underside of your tongue creates a different feeling. If you can do this whilst pressing gently on the area between his balls and his bum, you'll be doing well.

The odd glance in his direction always increases his excitement. Eye contact can be tricky when you're down there, but an intense stare while you're doing the business always works a treat. If your hair is long enough, let it fall around his thighs and stomach. If you start to get jaw ache before he seems ready to orgasm, ask him to help you out. He can masturbate with one hand while you lick and suck his willy and balls. It's a good tactic if you're tiring and it also gives him control of his orgasm. What you do at the point of no return is up to you – let him come in your mouth, on your face or, if you really can't bear it, take his willy in your hand at the last second and give him a nice deep, wet kiss instead.

Masturbation

The art of fiddling about with one's own nether regions has always been considered a male preserve. After all, men have been doing it since birth, hyperventilating over the underwear section in their mum's mail-order catalogue while still in short trousers. After this they graduate to comparing size – at school, work and in the gym – trying to figure out the eternal question of whether it does or doesn't matter. Women, on the other hand (pun intended), have been more inclined to keep such matters to themselves... Or at least that was the case until Samantha popped up on Sex & The City, discussing double-headed dildos at the breakfast table along with the cereal and the weather. Nowadays sisters are doing it for themselves and talking about it too, although many women will tell you quite honestly that they really need someone else's hands or willy to turn them on.

Some women don't like the idea of a man indulging in this kind of DIY, regarding it as something that should be unseen and unheard, or worrying that it means they are not sexy enough. However, men will generally tell you that their knees would buckle and their head spin if they were lucky enough to catch even the merest glimpse of a woman in the act of 'pleasuring herself'.

Masturbating in front of your man is a sure fire way to get him to agree to almost anything, even going on holiday with you and your mum, or cleaning the toilet with his toothbrush. As a visual stimulant, it's about as foolproof as turning up drunk with a drop-dead

gorgeous model slung over your shoulder squealing, 'Fondle my tiny bottom all you like!', then dropping her on the bed next to him while you make him a sausage sandwich. It really is that good.

If you're not sure how to approach it, try performing a striptease for your partner. Kit yourself out in your pointiest stilettos, look him in the eye and tease him by bending down in front of him with your bottom inches from his face, lap dancer-style. Slide down your bra straps and knickers a little and then pull them back up again. With one leg on his shoulder if he's sitting (ditto if he's standing and you're double-jointed), finish by rubbing your boobs and giving

Advanced Techniques

yourself a little massage down below. He'll be coming quicker than a 100-metre sprinter on steroids.

When he's going down on you in bed, try gently massaging your clitoris while he's nibbling and licking away. Be sure to tell him you love what he's doing so that he doesn't think he's just been made redundant and that you can manage perfectly well without him. After a few seconds, put your hands back on his ears and he'll be at you like a cat lapping up the cream. Literally.

Top Tip: Ring him up late at night (unless he's told you he's got a really important meeting the next day or he's staying at his mum's) and have phone sex while you masturbate. Get him to tell you what to do to yourself and respond by actually doing it, (not filing your nails while watching the news). Tell him what you're doing and how it feels and the next time he sees you you're guaranteed great sex. He'll remember the conversation and know exactly what you'd like him to do next.

There are a few tricks of the trade that will guarantee a man has a mind-blowing orgasm when you masturbate him. You'll be glad to know none of them involve cooking a roast dinner or washing his football kit

1 Grasp the base of the willy with one hand. Stroke from bottom to top, and when you hit the top (not literally, that would just make him cry) release the willy, then bring the other hand to the bottom of the willy and repeat. It's a bit like milking a cow, only the other way up and with less chance of being kicked in the face.

2 Hold his willy with two well-lubricated hands at either side, as if warming your hands on a cup of coffee, then slowly rub up and down in opposite directions, building up speed gradually then slowing down again and repeating.

3 Gently press his willy back on to his stomach (obviously when he's lying down) and rub the base of your palm up over his balls and along the length of his willy. Repeat with the other hand.

Spicing Things Up

'Kinky' is a word that was once used to describe hair that refused to hang straight. Today, however, it carries different connotations and is more likely to be used in connection with bedroom antics. Talking of which, the strange thing about the word 'kinky' is that when it does crop up in conversation you are probably not in the bedroom anyway. People who boast to others that they're kinky probably aren't. They just think they are because they left the lights on once. As is often the case, it's the quiet ones you have to watch. And come to think of it, they'd probably be delighted if you did.

So just how do you spice up your sex life without appearing desperate to find your man attractive again? When boredom strikes and the man snoring in bed next to you has been doing so for the last six years, how do you avoid starting an affair in an attempt to make life more interesting? At the start of a relationship, when it comes to sex, it's usually a case of anytime and anywhere, but as time goes by daily life can become increasingly tedious – sometimes to the point where you can no longer wash his underpants or watch him eat his breakfast without feeling like stabbing him with a sharp pencil. Inevitably, things tend to settle into a routine. There's no need to turn the spare room into an S&M dungeon, or anything quite so drastic, but here are a few tips to get you back into the swing of things. Spontaneity is the key, fancy underwear comes a close second.

If you get in from work before him one night, take a luxurious bath, shave your legs, splash on a generous helping of your most expensive body lotion and step into your fanciest underwear (yes, even it's a Tuesday). Slide on your stilettos and, if it's wintry outside, turn up the heating or you will have to give up after ten minutes and put on something woolly. Pour two glasses of chilled wine and await the sound of his key in the door. At this point it is helpful not to have dinner in the oven – you don't want to be leaping up to check the roast potatoes every five minutes. When he comes in, adopt a sexy, lounging position and greet him with a smile and a glass of wine. Unless he's had a very bad day in the office, he should whip off his tie, take a gentlemanly sip of wine and proceed to ravish you with all the gusto of a Sumo wrestler.

> Sit him on a chair, put your leg up on the arm of it (you're wearing your highest heels, of course), lick your middle finger and rub your clitoris. Gradually lean in closer so that his face is level with your hips and he can take over.

Don't limit yourselves to sex in the bedroom. Creep up behind him when he's washing up – though on second thoughts, if he is washing up, you may prefer to let him finish it first – then kiss the back of his neck, put your arms around him and move your hands down to his crotch. He will get the message soon enough and unless he's particularly conscientious and in the middle of removing scrambled egg from the bottom of a pan, he will turn around and respond accordingly. Anyway, egg comes off more easily if left to soak for a while…

Ring up his office and book him a day off without his knowledge, telling those in the know to keep it quiet. Book yourself a day off, or better still, throw a sickie. On the morning in question, wake him up with the best blow job you've ever given in your life, or at least with a fairly good one – if he's really sleepy he won't know the difference. When he makes bleating noises about having to go to work, tell him he's got the day off, that it's all above board and that you're going to spend the whole morning, or even day, in bed. Naturally, you will have stocked up on croissants, exotic coffee, champagne and strawberries, and the local take-out menu will be stashed under the mattress in

readiness for later. Have lots of sex, followed by a snooze and more sex. Then order in some dinner. Perfect.

If you don't get much time together, make the effort to book a room in a good hotel in town, but make sure it doesn't involve a stressful drive to get there. Choose one with a huge jacuzzi bath, crisp cotton sheets and fabulous room service. Repeat the steps described above, but without feeling guilty about messing up the sheets and not having to wash the dishes afterwards. If you've paid top dollar, you can feel entitled to get your money's worth, even if that means using all the towels at once and leaving the TV on just because you're not paying for the electricity. Your essential kit will consist of a silk scarf for blindfolding each other (during sex, not when answering the door to room service), handcuffs (of the pink, fluffy variety, unless he's a policeman, in which case use his), your best underwear and your highest heels.

Just leave your inhibitions at home.

Fantasies

Before we go any further (literally), it is important to point out that fantasies are often best left as just that. However, discussing your innermost thoughts with your partner (rather than with your boss or the postman), can sometimes add a gentle frisson to your relationship, whether you need it or not.

There are good and bad ways of introducing your fantasies. If you have several, it's best to introduce them one at a time. Simply saying 'Here's Johnny Depp, he's come for tea and then he's going to shag me while you do the washing up', is not the best option. A conversation with your partner on the subject of fantasies could lead to him asking, 'What would you really like me to do to you if a) money was no option, b) I had a much bigger willy (that's a lie – no man would ever say that), or c) we didn't live with your parents?' To which you might reply, 'Take me to Hawaii for a month and feed me mangoes while wearing nothing but a flower garland to preserve your modesty'. This would be acceptable, unlike, 'Well, come to think of it, I'd like it if you had enough money to leave the country at a moment's notice, never to return', which would not be, however accurate.

Telling him you've always had a big thing for his Dad, his best friend, his brother or his boss is simply off the agenda, no matter how hard you find it to contain yourself when you visit his parents for Sunday lunch. Fantasies involving actors or pop stars who are unlikely ever to cross your path are a safer if rather 'so what?' bet. Famous people are fancied by almost everyone you meet – that is what they're there for. Discuss what you would like to do with David Beckham or The Incredible Hulk with your girlfriends, but any fantasy shared with your partner should really involve him or he will feel left out.

It is important to ease him into your fantasy. Don't simply blurt out that you would like him to wear your underwear or sport a dog collar. Try and check out the situation by dropping relevant hints. Say something like, 'Goodness, my G-string is just soooo comfortable!' and monitor his response. If he says, 'I'd rather have dental surgery than wear one of those' you know not to go any further. Try proposing that you blindfold him, or dress up for him, preferably as a naughty nurse or Catwoman rather than as a gorilla. Alternatively, you could propose acting as his slave for the day, while he whips your backside with a cat o'nine tails. He may want to dress up himself, possibly even as a gorilla. Ease in the more risqué stuff subtly and gradually, such as dressing in PVC from head to toe and stomping all over his back in six-inch heels, or telling him you want him to wee on you. Although, why anyone would want to go in that particular direction remains a mystery to many, but, as they say, each to her own.

If your fantasy involves dressing up for him in more than the usual stockings and suspenders, try donning some of the following available in all good sex shops near you:

A French maid's outfit

A PVC nurse's uniform with mini skirt or dress

A PVC catsuit or rubber dress

Crotchless and peephole underwear

Failing any of the above, you could attempt to dress up as his favourite film star – as long as it's Audrey Hepburn and not Sylvester Stallone.

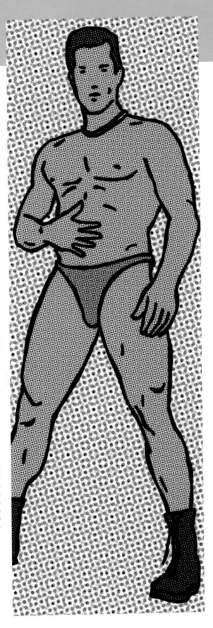

love in the dark

Sex Toys

There was a time when you could only purchase sex toys by disguising yourself with dark glasses, a large hat and a raincoat. Communication was via a nod or shake of the head as you sidled in through a door beneath a neon sign flashing ominously 'Adults Only. Dirty, Filthy, Bad Stuff. We Will Tell Your Mother'. As a result, many people simply didn't bother. These days, however, things have come a long way, so to speak. With the invention of upmarket sex shops selling diamond-encrusted (ouch, perhaps not) vibrators or fancy negligées retailing at the price of a small house in suburbia, there's no excuse not to explore different avenues (unintentional euphemism) in your sex life.

The Internet also gives you access to all sorts of fancy gadgets, the names of which link words you would never have imagined together, such as 'love' and 'balls', for example. Your goods will arrive on your doorstep wrapped discreetly in plain paper. Nobody need ever know what your parcel contains, unless the postman has such a hard time squeezing it through the letter box that the contents spill out, presenting an interesting spectacle at which your neighbours can either gawp or scream, depending on the nature of your order.

If you've never used a vibrator before, go easy on yourself and pick a small one. Don't head straight for the '10-Inches of Man Pleasure' or you could be put off for life. You can buy lipstick-sized vibrators that simply slip into your handbag (as well as your vagina). But if you grab the wrong one, don't blame the manufacturer if your Pink Frost lippie isn't doing much for you.

The most widely known and instantly recognizable vibrator, the 'Hey, Mum! I've got one of those!' is the Rabbit, made famous by Sex In The City's Samantha, queen of, well, sex. It is pink, with tiny rabbit ears (not real ones, sadly) that tickle your clitoris and has a weird, rotating section in the middle, full of coloured plastic beads. The problem is that not many men will be able to compare with it, unless they request some bizarre plastic surgery, so don't get too used to it or his non-rotating, bead-free, earless willy may become just too dull.

Involve your partner, too. Get him to use it on you, not just in your vagina but on your nipples, around your anus and inner thighs, as part of foreplay. Just don't let him think you prefer it to the real thing, even if you do.

How To Choose The Right Sex Toy For You

Just like shopping for shoes, what fits one woman snuggly might just rub another up the wrong way.

Vibrators are designed to stimulate the clitoris and vagina, with the vibrating motion setting off orgasm (hopefully) by holding it or rubbing it against the clitoris. Dildos, on the other hand, are better if you orgasm easily through penetration – they can be anything from 5 inches to over a foot long (ouch!). There hasn't been a vibrator invented yet that can put up shelves and make you a cup of tea after sex, but then there aren't many men who do that anyway. What vibrators do save you from is an STD or a phone call that never comes (unlike you). And of course, a cold winter's evening can always be brightened up with a glass of wine, the lights dimmed low and an early night with your magic wand. They're not designed to be a substitute for a relationship but they're good fun to have around whether you're in one or not.

If you're too embarrassed to go out and buy something specific, or if you can't face putting it on your Christmas list, make do with household items. A spot of lubricant and a round-headed deodorant bottle (with the lid on tight), a cucumber, courgette or zucchini, a candle (long and thin rather than a tea-light) – any of these will do. However, wash it thoroughly before and after use and don't put it in the stir-fry. Always bear in mind that arriving at the A&E department of the hospital with half a cucumber in one hand and the other half in a very private place can be extremely embarrassing .

Don't feel prudish if you're not turned on by the thought of a 12-inch vibrating member or having your best necklace shoved up your bottom. Some of us need another human with real sweat, body heat and skin to get us going. Sex toys can be fun, but they're not designed to cuddle up to afterwards.

love in the dark

Orgasms Explained

Orgasms are really, really good. There, will that do? Well, perhaps a little more detail is required. Just as discovering why great white sharks sometimes bite chunks out of surfboards instead of seals, finding out more about the workings of your body can be fascinating. And, at last you will understand why men always roll over and go to sleep after sex.

Orgasms happen in four stages:

1 The arousal stage

Your brain knows that having your neck nibbled or your inner thighs stroked is a good thing. This triggers the initial excitement, making you feel a little wobbly, and you may start writhing slightly. This is when you'll decide whether he's worth carrying on with or whether to get up and re-organise your spice rack. If he's good, all thoughts of cleaning or tidying will go out the window and you'll be on the way to orgasm. Let's just hope he can keep up the good work.

2 The plateau

As things get going, your heart rate speeds up and your blood pressure rises. It's not that different from how you would feel if you caught an intruder in your house, but a lot nicer hopefully. Your breathing becomes more rapid, that funny little red rash, or more accurately 'flush', appears on your neck, and your body temperature starts hotting up. You will now be begging him to penetrate you, so hopefully he will more than ready to do so.

It might come (excuse the pun) more naturally to close your eyes as you orgasm, but try looking intently at your partner as you come and likewise, as he does. Don't go cracking any jokes at this point; just enjoy the moment and if it happens for you both at the same time, you're guaranteed a spectacular ending.

3 The orgasm itself

The third stage only happens if your boyfriend has aroused you sufficiently during the first two. In other words, not every woman will have an orgasm, and if he doesn't keep up the good work in stage three, you certainly have no chance. A phone call from your Mum or the dog jumping on the bed at this point will have the same disappointing result. Men, on the other hand, are able to block all that stuff out, just as they can block us out when we are saying things they don't want to hear. If things are going well, however, your major and minor muscles will begin to contract, nerve endings will send waves of contractions through the pelvic floor muscles and you might even start to hyper-ventilate. Orgasms can last anywhere between three and ten seconds, but if you're watching an action movie at the same time, make that minutes rather than seconds.

4 The 'Zzzzzz' bit

Blood pressure, heart rate and breathing all return to normal, blood drains back from your genitals and, after about half an hour, you'll be ready to go again or demand a cup of tea, while he's already far away in the land of nod. It's all to do with science, so don't give him a hard time (nudge nudge); just enjoy the peace and quiet until he starts snoring. This is not a good time to say, 'What are you thinking, darling?' and expect the reply to be 'How much I love you.' If he is not fast asleep already, he will be thinking, 'I've just had sex. Cool.' That's how the male brain works. Honest.

Playing It Safe

Staying safe in this context doesn't mean avoiding kitchen fires or not climbing up wobbly ladders. Sexual safety is what's on the agenda. Being in the throes of passion may lead you to do all sorts of things you wouldn't normally dream of. Beware of calling your partner by your ex-boyfriend's name, or telling someone you've just met that you love them, when what you really mean is that you love what they're doing to you at that moment. What the excitement of the moment should never do is allow you to lose sight of the fact that safe sex is the responsibility of each and every one of us.

Along with all the various types of contraceptive pills, injections, IUDs, patches and, no doubt soon, a contraceptive kitten that administers oestrogen by licking you on the hand, condoms remain the best bet. Used on their own they'll protect you against sexually transmitted diseases (mmm, appetising), while used with other forms of contraception, such as the pill, you're practically 100% protected from both babies and nasty germs. Add a spermicidal lubricant or condoms containing spermicide into the equation and you'll probably be more protected than the crown jewels in the Tower of London.

Male condoms carry around a 2% failure rate, but if you're not lubricated, or if they aren't lubricated during sex, it's possible for them to burst due to the friction involved. Just make sure you use a lubricant specifically designed for use with condoms. Don't use baby oil as oil-based products can dissolve rubber.

Always check the expiry date on condoms, open the packet carefully (if you have those plastic three-inch false nails, get him to do it, unless, of course, he has

▶▶▶ If you've been in a relationship for a while and are considering stopping using condoms, both you and your partner should visit a sexual health clinic and have a general sex MOT. You must have a clean bill of health before giving condoms the heave-ho, and this only works if neither of you have unprotected sex with anyone else, so behave!

I Don't Like The Look Of That...

Sexually transmitted diseases (STDs) come in all guises, but the first signs that something's wrong is a bad smell, discharge, itching or unexplained lumps or bumps in the genital area. Occasionally it might turn out to be an ingrowing hair or harmless spot or boil (mmm, nice) which can be caused by over heating in the nether regions or non-cotton underwear chafing against the skin. You may have an infection which is easy to treat, but you could have something more serious. It's imperative that you tell your partner immediately if you suspect something's wrong so that he can get checked out as well. Anything resembling miniscule cauliflowers around the vaginal or anal passage could be genital warts, any red, sore blisters might be herpes and a seriously whiffy discharge could be anything from thrush to chlamydia. All need to be looked at and treated by a professional – don't ignore it.

them too) and make sure one of you holds firmly onto the condom at the base of his willy before he withdraws. Keeping him inside you until his erection deflates might cause sperm to leak from the condom.

There are so many types of condom available that it's almost as exciting as choosing a new pair of shoes. Well, maybe not quite. Ribbed or dotted types can increase friction, but they do need a good lubricant. If you think you're allergic to latex, go for polyurethane condoms and apply your favourite lubricant, whether oil-based or not. Flavoured condoms can actually be quite pleasant and not just during oral sex (try the strawberry – it's just like bubblegum!). They leave a nice fruity post-coital waft in the room. If a condom does burst or get lost inside you (it can happen if your boyfriend doesn't hold onto it when he withdraws), or if you have a lapse of common sense and don't use a condom in the first place, the morning after pill is an option. Available from chemists without prescription in some countries, it should be taken within 72 hours. If you suspect you may have picked up something nasty – sores, blisters, itchiness or swelling in the genital area are indications that you might have – go straight to your doctor and don't have sex in the meantime. An annual 'sex MOT' or check-up is a good idea – get yourself thoroughly checked out at a family planning clinic or by your doctor, just to be on the safe side. It's worth enduring a five-minute cringe in return for an all-clear.

◀◀◀ **For Her**

NOTE: For the best luminous results, expose the illustrations on the following pages to light for a couple of minutes before switching the light off ▶ ▶

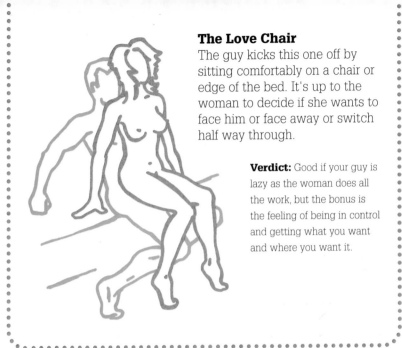

The Love Chair

The guy kicks this one off by sitting comfortably on a chair or edge of the bed. It's up to the woman to decide if she wants to face him or face away or switch half way through.

Verdict: Good if your guy is lazy as the woman does all the work, but the bonus is the feeling of being in control and getting what you want and where you want it.

The Workout

Not for the weak-willed, this is an intensely physical position that will leave you aching where you didn't know you had muscles. The position itself offers little more stimulation than the others, but if you want to keep fit, this one's for you.

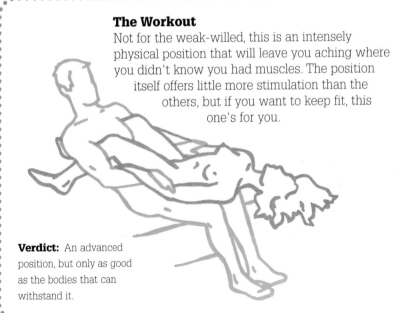

Verdict: An advanced position, but only as good as the bodies that can withstand it.

The Recliner

Just like The Love Chair, this position is good for the woman who wants control. However, it is a little more intimate and if you're on a springy bed, the guy is able to assist with a little bit of bounce.

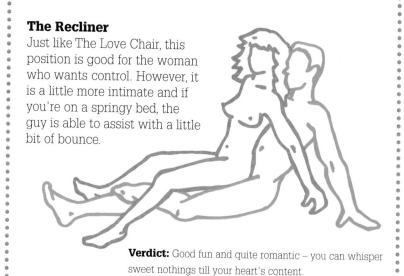

Verdict: Good fun and quite romantic – you can whisper sweet nothings till your heart's content.

The Bridge

The most advanced position in this book, you will earn a gold star if you are able to achieve it. The woman needs to resist putting her weight (or balance) on the guy as this is a difficult position for him to hold for a long time. Once ready, the woman is in control of the motions.

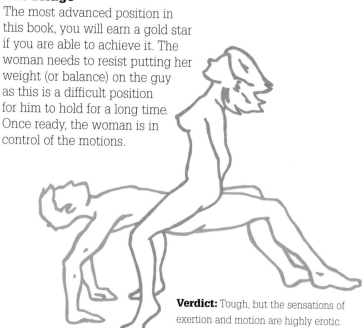

Verdict: Tough, but the sensations of exertion and motion are highly erotic.

The Lap Dance

Similar to The Love Chair, this position requires the guy to lift himself off the bed and gyrate with the woman on top. This requires some physical strength so the woman should be wary and not place all her weight on his lap.

Verdict: Sensual, but physically demanding – best keep this one for special occasions.

The Love Hug

A very intense, intimate and sensuous position where the woman is in control of the gyrations. The guy has to keep his pelvis in a raised position or there is a danger of his manhood disappearing between his legs.

Verdict: Very lovey-dovey – try some variations with the guy kneeling or sitting cross-legged.

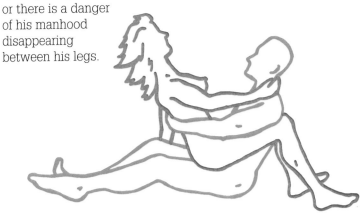

The Heave-Ho

The guy thrusts from the kneeling position which offers perfect penetration. The woman can support herself if the guy gets too tired or if he's fit, she has a free hand to help herself along.

Verdict: Erotic and deep, this position takes a strong man with stamina.

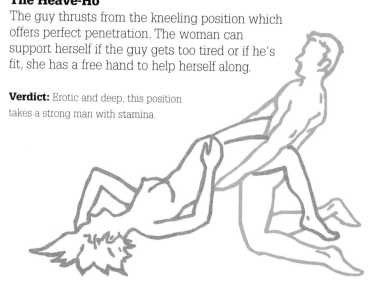

The Butterfly

This erotic, woman-on-top position is great for a bit of domination. When your man is ready, simply straddle him and guide his manhood inside you. It's up to you how much you wriggle and you may find some light bondage will increase his sensuality.

Verdict: Simply the best if you like a woman in control of the trouser department.

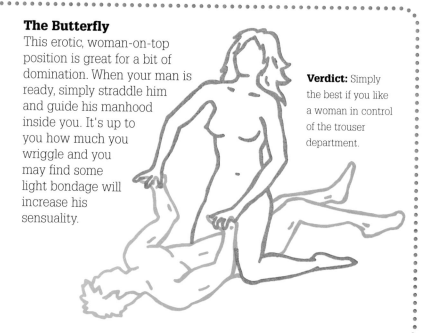

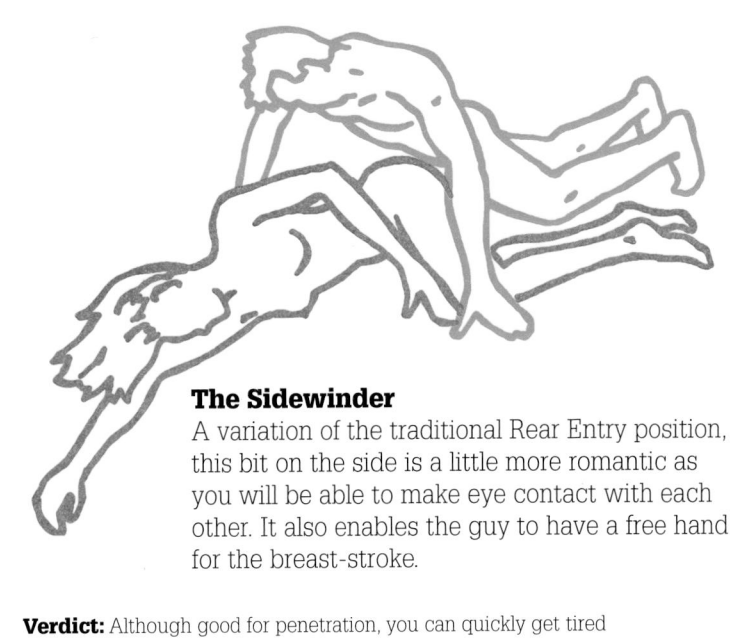

The Sidewinder

A variation of the traditional Rear Entry position, this bit on the side is a little more romantic as you will be able to make eye contact with each other. It also enables the guy to have a free hand for the breast-stroke.

Verdict: Although good for penetration, you can quickly get tired in this position and become uncomfortable.

Lift and Pump

There is no better position for a woman to climax than this one. As the guy is lifting her up from the bed her vaginal muscles are tensed – making the perfect scenario for a screaming orgasm. What's more, the guy is improving his physique by working out on his six-pack.

Verdict: Good for him and great for her – the perfect all-round sex improver.

The Back Door

Also known as the Rear Entry, this is a great position for both vaginal or anal sex (if you are feeling brave enough). The angle of attack from the guy is almost directly on to the G-spot and the woman can also pleasure herself if she wants to.

Verdict: The best all-round position for a highly charged night of passion and orgasm.

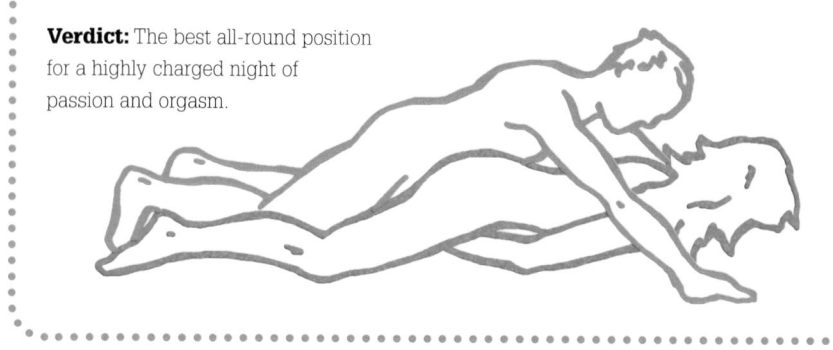

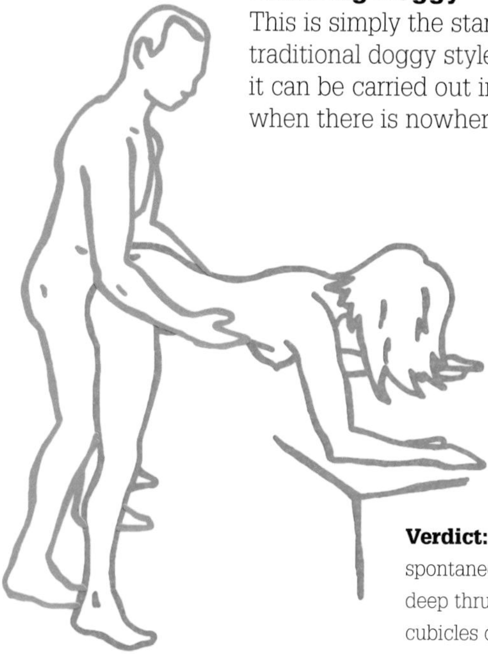

Standing Doggy

This is simply the standing version of the traditional doggy style. The benefit is that it can be carried out in confined places or when there is nowhere to lie down.

Verdict: Great for spontaneous moments of deep thrusting passion in cubicles or lavatories.

The 69 Shuffle

A very intimate pose that will leave you begging for more. However, it's not for the prudish... you will get an eyeful of your partner's backside throughout this process.

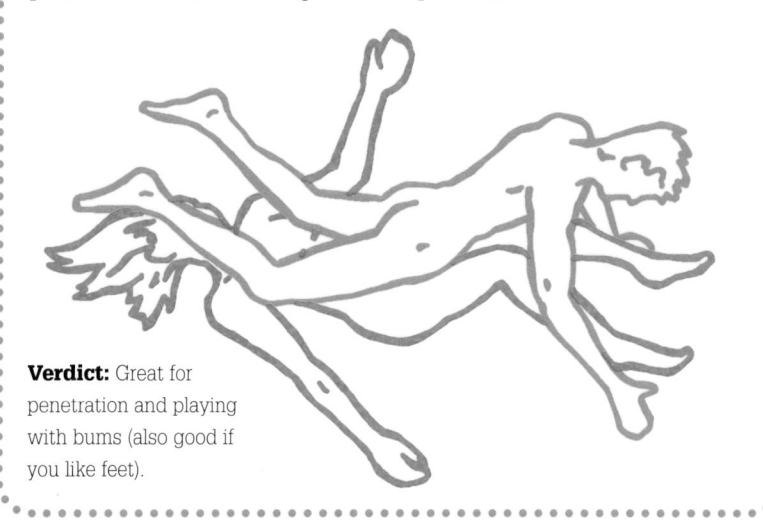

Verdict: Great for penetration and playing with bums (also good if you like feet).

Bedside Bonkers

An easy position to achieve (provided your 'bits and pieces' are on the same level). Try shifting around on the bed until you are both comfortable and find your natural rhythm. Don't forget to make intense and erotic eye-contact with each other.

Verdict: One of the best positions for deep penetration and pleasurable to both parties.

Kneeling Doggy Style
Try this variation of the traditional 'on all-fours' doggy style. The woman stands by the edge of the bed, or table, or firm surface and the guy comes in from behind.

Verdict: Requires a lot of energy, but the deep penetration makes it worthwhile.

The Missionary
Although this position is the most common, it does little for vaginal stimulation or penetration. So why not try the same position but raise the woman's legs a little or place a pillow under her bum?

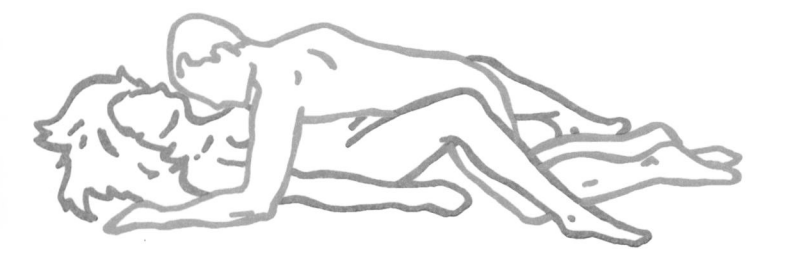

Verdict: Good for romantic intimacy and for use on the first date.

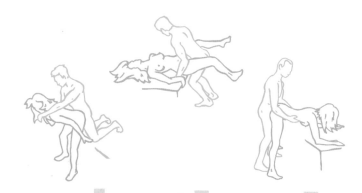

love in the dark

a his and hers activity book

with glow-in-the-dark features

Juliette Wills

HarperCollins*Entertainment*

An Imprint of HarperCollins*Publishers*

How Sexy Are You?

You don't have to look like a movie star or David Beckham to be sexy (although admittedly, it does help). Being sexy is all about the individual – how sexy you are to that special someone. One woman might find spending all weekend beneath the bonnet of a 1957 Cadillac and emerging with oily hands a total turn on, while another might have packed her things and left you before you can say 'fan belt'.

Some women will admit that size doesn't matter and even that they prefer a small willy. Others – the sensible ones, of course – say the contrary and will not even give the time of day to a man who isn't packed like a porn star. So, one person's definition of what is sexy might not be another's, but there are some looks that will mark you out as, well, generally not that sexy at all, and others that will make her putty in your hands. There are, however, a number of obviously unattractive traits, such as those outlined below.

The Golden Rules Each to her own when it comes to what a woman thinks is sexy, but for most women, the following are not:

1 Dirty hair. We know there's the unkempt, 'bed' hair look, which actually involves a lot of work and sweet-smelling hair products. But simply not washing it isn't the same thing at all!

2 Smelly bed sheets. Yes, some women like a man's 'natural' scent, but that's generally right after he's scored a goal or put up some shelves, not three months' worth of farting and sweating while you sleep.

3 Bad clothes. That means manky tracksuit bottoms, whiffy trainers, socks with holes in the toes or novelty boxer shorts. Nobody wants to see Santa in July..

4 Making her sleep in the **wet patch**, kicking her in your sleep, asking her to make the tea in the morning when she's staying at yours and forgetting her name. Worse still, calling her by the wrong name. If in doubt, just address her with 'Hey'. Or even 'Oi!'

'Sex' factor or 'ex' factor?

When dressing for a dinner date with a new woman, what are you most likely to wear?

a) A tight T-shirt which shows off your pecs, a whole bottle of aftershave and Cuban heels to give you an extra few inches... height-wise.

b) A well-ironed shirt, a splash of expensive cologne and a smile.

c) Whatever you wake up in from the night before, even if it's your pyjamas.

When you want to make the first move, do you:

a) Shove your hand up her skirt, press your mouth on hers and hope for the best.

b) Stroke her neck, hold her face with one hand and slowly lean in for a kiss.

c) Put on a porn film and hope that does the trick.

Your idea of going down on a woman is:

a) A chance to put the condom on while she's not looking, so you can get on with proper sex as soon as possible.

b) Heaven. In fact, you're honoured that she lets you and you savour every lick and nibble.

c) Terrifying. I mean, she might not have had a wash. And then there's pubic hairs, they could choke a man. And I might strain my neck.

When discussing fantasies with your partner, you're most likely to say:

a) 'I've always had a thing for your Mum. And your sister. And your cat's not bad either.'

b) 'You're so special to me I'd whisk you away to a desert island, gather coconuts for you and spear fish for dinner despite the risk of a shark attack.'

c) 'I'd love it if you'd help me catalogue my Star Trek DVDs.'

conclusion **Mostly a's:** Easy tiger! Where did you learn the art of seduction? Behind the bike sheds? You need to read this book thoroughly. Now! **Mostly b's:** What a gent. That must explain how so many ugly blokes get decent looking girlfriends. **Mostly c's:** Mmm, how romantic – have you ever thought about exactly why you're still single?

The Etiquette Of Seduction

Women don't mess about. When they're interested, they'll let you know pretty quickly. When they're not, they'll let you know even quicker. There are plenty of signs that indicate when a woman is keen and just as many that show she thinks you're hideous/a fool/look like her little brother. It's up to you to familiarise yourself with what constitutes a come on and what is a clear 'Back off'. It's not that difficult, but it can be confusing. Understandable when some women are so rude they'll dismiss you with a flick of the hand, while others are so polite they'll listen to you waffling on about the size of your car engine, when they'd rather be boiling their own kidneys. So, here is a guide to spotting whether you're in with a chance or not.

Top Tip: Listen to her when she's talking, even if she's been going on about her cat for the last half an hour. Buy her a drink, but if she asks for orange juice, don't try and bully her into drinking a beer. Women don't like being told what to do, and it's gentlemanly to show you respect what she wants, even if you do want to get her so drunk she can't remember her name let alone yours.

◀ *Eye want you – the warm smile and sparkling eye-contact with you (not your mate) are sure signs that you're on to a winner.*

Good Signs

1 When you approach her, she smoothes down her skirt or hair, deftly undoes a button on her top, or runs her tongue across her teeth to check for lipstick marks.

2 Her mobile phone rings and she turns it off to carry on talking to you. However, if it's her Mum/best mate/dog and she asks you to speak to them, she's a bit too keen!

3 She strokes her neck, shoulders or chest, flicks her hair, or nips to the ladies to apply more lipstick, yet only takes two minutes to do it!

4 She gives your her mobile number – and her home number – and her e-mail address – and personally puts the piece of paper in your pocket so that she knows you've got it.

5 She touches your hand or your arm, brushes imaginary fluff from your shirt, leans in to whisper in your ear and circles the top of her glass with her forefinger in a 'Come hither, this could be your willy' motion.

Bad Signs

1 She turns her back on you, says 'Talk to the hand, loser' or slowly inches away from you the closer you get.

2 Her mobile phone rings and she answers it, then says, 'It's the taxman/bank manager/grim reaper' yet still carries on talking – for at least half an hour.

3 She looks over your shoulder at another man, or worse still, a blank wall, says she's going to the ladies to 'powder her nose' but then doesn't come back. Ever.

4 When you ask for her number she says 'My phone's just been disconnected', 'I live on a kibbutz' or 'My husband might answer if he's off duty. He's just been promoted to the Vice Squad'.

5 She keeps her hands in her lap or over her drink as though she thinks you might be trying to drop a sleeping tablet in it. She recoils as you lean in to talk to her, implying that you may well have the breath of a dead dog.

Foreplanning For Foreplay

It's no good striking it lucky with a member of the opposite sex if she loses interest rapidly as soon as you take her home. You might be forgiven for thinking that meeting a decent woman is the hardest part of the whole seduction thing, but you'd be wrong. Keeping her is the really tough bit. It all starts back at your place, whether you are on a proper date or enjoying a 'pop in for coffee' moment. Apart from actually buying some decent coffee and fresh milk (a well-known hiccup), you need to make sure that the woman involved will not be heading for the door before you have even managed to say, 'Make yourself comfortable'.

There are a few very obvious things that you must clear away. Put porn mags under the bed rather than by the toilet. A woman really doesn't want to see this kind of literature on a first date unless she's actually starring in it. Get rid of take-out cartons and pizza boxes, make sure your dirty clothes are picked up from the floor (no, don't just throw them on a chair) and ensure you have at least introduced the floor to the vacuum at some point during the last year.

Women will almost always show their interest in you indirectly. This is a polite way of saying that they'll go through all your belongings the minute your back is turned, in search of clues to your real personality, as well as your past, present and future. Bank statements, photos of ex-girlfriends in dog collars and thigh-length boots, the odd court summons, passports giving away your real date of birth and receipts for clothes from final sales in discount warehouses – all these should be burned or hidden well away from prying eyes.

Women will zoom in on your CD collection, looking for signs of instability, too much stability, an uncool past or an uncool present. It is worth having a flick through your DVD collection to prune it accordingly – it might be wise to hide your complete collection of Rambo films or your well-worn copy of Riverdance. You must be getting the idea by now.

A clean kitchen is next on the agenda. Women like peering into other people's refrigerators out of sheer curiosity. You can tell a lot about a man by its contents (or lack of them). If it's full of beer, it won't take long to work out that you drink lots of it. If it's full of mouldy fruit and cheese that has been there for weeks rather than a choice blue variety from the specialist French cheese shop, she'll think you're a

▲ *Love nest or smelly mess? Plan ahead to get your girl in bed by keeping your room clean and tidy at all times.*

slob. If the refrigerator is clean and stocked with butter, eggs, bacon, milk and fruit juice, she'll see you as a good bet. At least you'll be able to knock up some breakfast the following morning.

If it's filthy and contains nothing but the remnants of last week's leftover pizza, you'll be lucky to get a farewell wave, never mind a goodnight kiss.

You don't have to hide your entire life away, just seek, find and destroy those items you know could put her off in a major way. Tidy up a bit, wash your bed linen, make sure there really is coffee in the house. She may be play it cool and accuse you of inviting her in under false pretences, Finally, clean the bath. Any more than that and you might turn into a girl yourself.

Top Tip: Encourage her to undress you. It happens quite often in movies, but rarely in real life. Place her hands on your tie, shirt buttons, belt and if she gets stuck on a tricky buckle, help her out, but then encourage her to carry on. However, try and get your socks off before she starts undoing your jeans. There's nothing worse than a man baring all... in his socks.

Erogenous Zones

Most men still zoom straight in on a woman's nipples, treating the rest of her body as if it were covered in goose fat and her breasts the only available parts with which to fiddle. Playing with her nipples like someone who has just put a coin in a pinball machine is not a good technique. Gentle nibbling, licking and sucking are fine, but that flicking motion is not advisable. And don't ignore her thighs, stomach, hips, neck and shoulders. Every woman is different. Some enjoy having their neck nibbled, others like having their thighs stroked and some are in heaven when their stomach is kissed. It's a very individual thing, but you are unlikely to encounter a woman who would lodge a complaint about any of these.

▶▶▶ The **major** female erogenous zones are as follows:

Lips

Clitoris

Nipples

Entrance to her vagina

▶▶▶ The **minor** female erogenous zones include the following:

Back of her neck

Earlobes

Inner thighs

Stomach

Fingers

It's always nice when a man pays attention to the less obvious parts of a woman's anatomy, such as gently kissing her eyelids or slowly nibbling on her tummy, hips and inner thighs. You can't beat turning her on her front and kissing and licking your way down her spine to the small of her back, nibbling on her buttocks, then turning her back over for a deep, passionate kiss. As with men, the anus is a very sensitive area, but not all women like a man to go there. If you're not sure, test the water with a lubricated finger, gently circling the anus. If she pushes against you, she likes it. If she backs off with the speed of a gazelle, pulls the covers up to her face and calls a taxi, she probably doesn't.

Sensual Massage

A massage needn't be a full on, towels on the floor, candlelit affair – it can be just as nice to have a five-minute shoulder rub after a hard day at work. However, every woman will appreciate your undivided attention lavished upon her body, provided you can tear yourself away from the sports channel for half an hour. First, make sure the room is warm – shivering is not very relaxing – and dim the lights. Ask her to lie face down, naked, but don't forget that she's there and wander off to tidy your sock drawer.

Massage Techniques

Warm the oil or lotion in the palms of your hands before applying it to her skin, working in large circles from the small of her back outwards. Knead gently with your palms as you work up her back. Don't apply too much pressure to start with, but increase it gradually, checking with her that it feels good and is not too hard. Apply a little extra pressure on any knotted or tensed muscles that you notice, using your thumbs and finger tips. Keep adding lotion as you go so that her skin doesn't become dry and burn with the friction. Little kisses on the back of her neck as you work won't go unappreciated, and will make sure you keep her hair out of the way of the oil or lotion.

When you have finished her back, move down over her buttocks, inner thighs and backs of the legs and then ask her to turn over. Kneel astride her without actually sitting down on her, and gently stroke her stomach, shoulders and arms. Rub her fingers and hands in long gentle strokes from the wrist to the finger tips, and then massage the inside of her thighs gently, with light strokes, until she's wriggling with pleasure. Don't be afraid to give her feet a nice rub as well, pulling gently on the toes as you did the fingers, but not too vigorously. You don't want to pull them out of their sockets. Now would be a good time to go down on her, so keep your oily hands away from where you're ready to feast – massage oil might smell good but it doesn't taste so – and get to work.

Why do women spend so much time at the hairdresser's? It might not just be for the cut or colour. Sit her in front of you, place your hands on either side of her head (unless, of course, she's just come back from the salon in which case she'll go mad at you for messing her hair up) and with fingers and thumbs, massage her head quite firmly in a circular motion with her head tipped back slightly in your lap.

Top Tip: Leave her knickers on when you begin, but then remove them slowly when you're ready to pay attention to her bum and thighs.

Sex Foods

We all know that the sight of a man cooking breakfast, lunch or dinner is enough of a turn-on for a woman in itself – unless it's a microwave meal for one or boil-in-the-bag cod. But if you're really clever, you can knock up a meal rich in flavour and aphrodisiac properties. It is the

▶▶▶ Asparagus

One of the most sensual foods around – the fact that it should be eaten with your fingers, melted butter dripping from the tips, and requires much licking of the lips and fingers makes it an ideal prelude to sex. According to an ancient herbalist, asparagus arouses your sexuality to boot.

▶▶▶ Chocolate

We all know this is available as body paint, but you can also use it to achieve to a more subtle erotic effect by feeding your girlfriend chocolates with your fingers. Let her suck each chocolate from them as you put it in her mouth, or trace over her body with a piece of chocolate and lick it off as you go. Her body temperature will melt the chocolate as you move it over her. This will work nicely with a handful of expensive plain chocolates, but probably won't carry the same erotic charge with a family-sized bar of chunky milk.

perfect double whammy as far as seduction is concerned, without even having to switch the oven on. A bottle of champagne in the fridge and a tub of ice-cream in the freezer is more than enough to get you started.

▶▶▶ Alcohol

It may be obvious, but champagne isn't the only drink worth spilling on a woman. Try frozen cocktails from the supermarket – the ice cold will have her wriggling in mock pain. Then as you lick pina colada or marguerita mix from her body, the warmth of your tongue should keep her happy. If either of you are teetotal, don't try substituting a cup of coffee – you could both end up in the burns unit of the local hospital.

▶▶▶ Cream and ice cream

Both have a high milk content, providing calcium, essential for those strong nails to drag down your partner's back in the throes of passion. It also helps out with muscle contractions during orgasm. Yes, really! Oh, and it tastes pretty good too. Squirty cream from a pressurised can is fun for both of you to use, but ice cream containing chunks of nuts or butterscotch is best avoided – you don't really want to be caught frantically chewing away while she's waiting patiently beside you. You should just be using your tongue to lick it off. Then make sure she has her daily dose of calcium and kiss her deeply with ice cream on your tongue.

More Than
Two Players

Just like a long car journey, a threesome takes a lot of planning and preparation. Less petrol, maybe, but hang on to the map as you might need to navigate your way out of a tricky, not to mention sticky, situation.

Don't rush into a threesome, there are a number of things you need to take into consideration, not least of which are the personal feelings of the people involved. First of all, are you sure your relationship is strong enough to involve a third person, even if it is only a one-off occasion? How do you think you will feel watching your girlfriend give another man a blow job, for instance? The whole thing could result in turmoil, when all you wanted to do was spice things up a little and try out something new. It has been known for one of the original couple to fall in love with the third person on the strength of the latter's performance. Before you know it, that three for the price of two label in the supermarket could become an unwelcome reminder of the biggest mistake in your (sex) life.

Many women fantasise about sex with two men, and some are not averse to trying out sex with their boyfriend and another woman. This may sound like a good idea to you as you'd enjoy watching the pair of them, willy in hand. However, what if your girlfriend were to find experimenting with the other woman so enjoyable that she was evidently considering becoming a

lesbian, and you were left seething on the sidelines? Sex with two men can have the same effect – though unless you've been hiding a big secret, it's unlikely that your girlfriend will be watching you have sex with the other man. It's more likely that the other guy might just be better at pleasing her than you are, leaving you begging her to stop making such noises of sheer contentment, or on the verge of punching him in the face.

Despite this, if you still decide to go ahead, getting completely sozzled to loosen inhibitions is not recommended, though a glass of something sparkling beforehand is a nice idea to break the ice. The third person should not be someone you've just met in the launderette. And how would you broach the subject, anyway? 'Hello, your jeans seem to be dry now, are you interested in numerology? My favourite number is three.' But nor should it be a buddy of yours either, as he could well serve as a constant reminder of the night you realised your girlfriend decided that size did matter after all and that your mate's got a better six pack than you.

One solution to finding the perfect participant for your ménage à trois is to

love in the dark

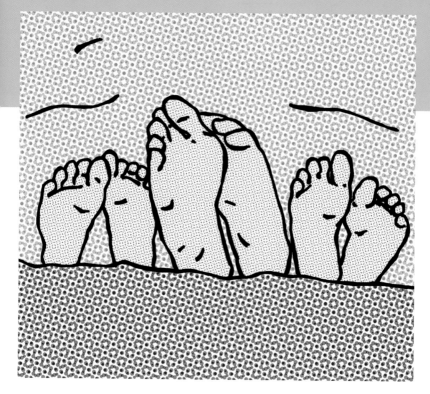

recruit someone from a swingers website over the Internet. There you can look at a photo (hopefully of him or her), and read a short blurb, 'Hi, I'm Andrew/Sandra and I enjoy urban chill out Latin jazz and wearing crotchless tights'. It's a good idea to arrange to meet the lucky winner in advance to check that you fancy her or, if it's a guy, to ask him which football team he supports. Other than that, it's fetish clubs or word of mouth, but handing out flyers advertising for participants is not advisable. It might just be best to talk about what you'd do and leave it at that. Threesomes can be complicated with all those elbows, feet and knees in the way. You could easily have someone's eye out.

Top Tip: If your partner is open minded enough to have a threesome in the first place and you've agreed the third person is going to be a woman, let her choose. The chances are that she'll have higher standards than you, and she'll also feel more in control of the situation.

Going Down?

Women are generally harder to please than men, so going down on a lady requires skill and stamina. It's like a game of football – if you want to score, learn the rules.

First of all, you need to make sure she's ready. There's no green light to give you a clue, so you'll have to read the signs for yourself. You've been kissing for a while, the kisses are getting harder and deeper and she's pushing herself towards you – things are looking good. Head for her stomach first, giving it gentle kisses. Then nibble on her hips, run your tongue up the inside of her thigh and come back up to kiss her on the lips again. Give her clitoris a little rub with your finger while you decide in which position you want her – on all fours or on her back. If she's lying down, gently lift her under the buttocks in order to tilt her slightly. Without actually blowing, breathe heavily on her clitoris, pressing on it with the tip of your tongue in a circular motion. Alternate tiny kisses with a deep thrusting of your tongue inside her. Some women enjoy being gently bitten on the outer lips of the vagina; you'll have to experiment to see if she's one of them, but a sudden 'Ouch!' will let you know if she's not.

You can also tell her she tastes good. Women always worry that they don't and reassurance will make her relax all the more, making your job easier. If your partner tastes like week-old cat food, however, don't come up for air spluttering and coughing and wiping your face – merely forget it for the time being and suggest a sensual shower before you next embark. Don't be afraid to use your fingers inside

Top Tip: If your partner is lying on her back, go down on her side-on, or, in other words, with your head between her legs and the back of your head to her. Your chin rubs against her clitoris, so please remember to shave unless you've got a nice soft beard like Santa Claus (there's nothing worse than three-day stubble rubbing against a woman's soft bits). If you're very lucky, she might find time to stroke your willy. If you're very, very good, she might even return the favour.

her while you lick and suck at the same time; this is often the best way for her to reach orgasm. It's a myth that women need half an hour of oral sex before they can orgasm – if you're doing it right she should come within a few minutes. When she does, there's no better feeling than you thrusting your tongue as deep as you can inside her. You can feel her shudder and she has something to push against. If she grabs your hair to pull you up, it doesn't necessarily mean she wants you to stop; it's more likely that she wants to kiss you for doing a good job and tell you she's ready for full-on sex.

Practise by all means, but not on another woman. Use a pot of yogurt. Seriously. Buy a pack of mini yogurts or fromage frais and lick the entire pot clean, using only your tongue. It will exercise your jaw and tongue and doesn't look too weird if you get caught out – you can always pretend you couldn't find a clean spoon...

▲ *Practice makes perfect – this simple exercise will strengthen your tongue muscles and make you great in the going down department!*

▶▶▶ 'A nuclear reactor is a lot like a woman. You just have to read the manual and press the right button.'

Homer Simpson

love in the dark

for him 19

Masturbation

Whilst a spot of DIY is simply part and parcel of a man's life from the day he knows what it means till the day he's either too old or tired to undo his trousers, it's always had a bad reputation among the ladies. You begin by hiding it from your Mum and simply graduate to hiding it from your girlfriend. True, it's not a good idea to ring her up at work and announce that you're off to the loo with a copy of Great Big Boobies but, at the right time and place, it can be something in which you can both indulge. The wrong time and the wrong place and you'll end up with a limp willy and a red face. On the other hand, get it right for both of you and it brings a whole new meaning to the term 'self service'.

▶▶▶ When It's OK To Help Yourself

1 At home, alone, in bed or in the shower or even on the sofa if the tissues are handy and the you're not expecting any visitors, such as your parents or the church group.

2 At the doctors when they need a sample of your man juices for medical reasons.

3 When you're trapped, alone, in a cave after a pot-holing accident and need to keep warm and alert.

Your partner might not like you masturbating over pictures of porn stars. In fact, most women don't like it. She'll probably feel insecure, think she needs to shave her pubic hair off and get nylon hair extensions for you to find her sexy. Reassure her that it isn't your reading material that really turns you on, it's her... and then tell her that when you come, you close your eyes and think of her.

▶▶▶ **Don't Even Think About It**

1 At home, in the kitchen, when your flatmate is trying to make a bacon sandwich, or even in your flatmate's bedroom because it's tidier than yours. No, no, no, no, no!

2 Over a dirty mag in front of your girlfriend as she's

trying to watch a soap, or study for an exam.

2 At a wedding (particularly yours), funeral, exam, driving test or any nerve-wracking situation where you need to 'relieve tension'. Take a deep breath or take up knitting instead.

Being able to pull off, excuse the pun, a bout of self-help is all very well, but how do you get around to incorporating it into your sex life? Will she be keen or will it just give her an inferiority complex, convincing her she's so hopeless at sex that you need to do it yourself?

Here's the answer: while you're in the throes of deep kisses and perhaps when you're fingers are beginning to work their way inside her vagina, reach for her hand and get her to play with herself. Some women are self-conscious and will refuse, while others will be as keen as mustard to help you out. You'll learn what she likes by watching what she does, and there's no bigger turn-on

for you than watching her making herself wet as even the nicest girls look a bit dirty when they do that. And in your eyes that can only be a good thing, no? You can then take the opportunity to lie down again, catch your breath and say hello to your little soldier while she's otherwise engaged. Some women love watching a man jack off, and she might even decide to help you out with her mouth, letting you do the hard work once you're in the swing of things. As things heat up, push your willy between her breasts (perhaps ask first) and if she seems happy enough, come all over them, or over her face if she agrees, but for goodness' sake, try not to get it in her eyes...

Spicing Things Up

Don't worry, we're not about to suggest that you start dripping hot wax on your chest to impress your lady, it's just that after the initial frenzied sex fest enjoyed by all couples in the first few months/weeks/days (delete as appropriate), things do tend to slow down a bit. You're tired, she's tired, there's ironing to be done, dinners to cook and sex often takes a back seat to everything else once domesticity starts to get the upper hand. So how do you put the spice back into your sex life without resorting to swinging through the window dressed as Tarzan rather than using the front door? Well, it's not as difficult as you might think, and sometimes doesn't even require that much energy or organisation, which as any woman knows, isn't generally a man's strong point anyway.

Instead of coming home from work and falling asleep with your Bart Simpson tie in your food and then sloping off to bed after the news, try and remember what it was like when you first met. You'd have sex before dinner and even let your pasta get cold because she excited you so much. That's dedication. Here are a few suggestions that won't leave you so exhausted that you're too tired to actually have sex afterwards.

How often do you tell your partner she looks beautiful? Maybe not too often if she's snoring on the sofa in her curlers, slippers and jogging pants, but if you're going out together – or more worryingly, she's going out without you – tell her she looks gorgeous. On no account tell her she just looks 'nice'. Nice is what grandparents say about sandwiches. If she's carefully made up and has done her hair it's not a good time to get amorous as she'll moan about getting her lipstick smudged and her dress creased. Just make sure you let her know what you're going to do with her when she gets back.

The next time you are getting ready to go out to dinner and she's wearing a skirt, suggest that she 'forgets' to wear any knickers. That way she'll get a nice refreshing breeze around her nether regions and you'll spend the evening not just salivating over your sirloin steak and crème caramel, but at the thought of her naked beneath her skirt. That will make things much more interesting for both of you when you accidentally 'drop' your knife under the table in the restaurant.

The Five Spices of Sexual Wisdom

1 Talk about your turn ons and turn offs

2 Do it differently and at different times

3 Dress sexy, look sexy, feel sexy

4 Try abstaining from sex and do massage instead

5 Learn to laugh and joke about what you do in bed

Then your fork. And then your spoon. You get the idea. Pop out in your lunch hour and buy her some nice underwear – and that doesn't mean from the charity shop or discount warehouse. Any good department store will sell sexy sets of bra, knickers, suspender belt and stockings. At this stage it might be a bit scary to bring home crotchless panties and a peep-hole bra, unless you know she'll play along (and you can never get a refund due to reasons of hygiene). You can make sure you buy the right size by checking the labels on her underwear, unless they're so old and faded that they're no longer legible. If you've got any doubts about what to buy, go for black rather than red (classy over, brassy) or compromise with leopard print – always a winner if you can track it down. Ask a girl in the office to wrap it in tissue paper for you if you're all fingers and thumbs and leave it on the bed for when she gets home. She should get the hint, particularly if you've already run her a bubble bath and handed her a glass of champagne/wine/meths, whatever gets her going.

▶ ▶ ▶ There are hundreds of websites to help you locate your local fetish club if you both fancy being more adventurous. Just bear in mind that you'll have to dress the part – and that doesn't mean no trainers – in some places you'll be expected to join in with activities for which you might not be prepared.

Fantasies

Fantasies are often best left as just that. However, discussing your innermost thoughts with your partner, as opposed to your Mum or the girl at the supermarket checkout, can sometimes do wonders for your relationship, even if it's already going great guns.

How best to broach the subject? Well, you could always try asking, 'Do you have any fantasies?' It might just do the trick, but equally, women being women, she may immediately get suspicious and answer with, 'I knew you fancied my sister, you bastard!' instead of, 'Why, yes, let me tell you all about them'.

Discuss your fantasies about other women with your mates or the Samaritans. Under no circumstances discuss bringing another woman into the equation with your partner unless she does so herself. Although she knows full well that your fantasy is to eat a 14-oz rump steak from Britney Spears' honey-skinned stomach, she won't be keen for you to say it out loud. The same goes for Kylie's or Cameron Diaz's tummy, just in case you're wondering.

On the other hand, bring your partner into the fantasy and she'll feel like the sexiest girl in the world, or at least the sexiest girl in your bed at that particular moment. Tell her how much you enjoy sex with her, how gorgeous she is and how you don't need fantasy situations to make things any better than they already are...

then wait a few seconds and launch straight into how you want to tie her to the bed with your football socks, gag her with your team's scarf and go and watch the Cup Final in peace. Actually, that was a joke. Well, some of it, at least. Tie her up by all means if she fancies it, and blindfold her too if she is willing, but make sure it's with something soft like a silk scarf . A bit of old string and a strip of gaffer tape are not the answer. See how she reacts and take it from there. Acceptable fantasies for any woman with a pulse would involve her going out without any knickers, wearing PVC or a nurse's uniform (rather than a hospital gown), or totally dominating you while you lie back and have a rest .

If her fantasy is for you to do the ironing, clean the car or collect her coat from the dry cleaners, you know you've got problems. She might want you to strip for her, which could – or, let's face it, would – make you look ridiculous. She may ask you to impersonate her favourite singer or actor, making you think you're in a rather bad game of charades and that unless you talk like Al Pacino she won't love you anymore.

Keep things simple if you're in the early stages of a relationship. Never appear at the front door dressed in full sex slave regalia if she's not expecting it. She'll either call the police or have a heart attack.

Top Tip: If you're a bit shy or embarrassed about sharing your fantasy because you don't know how she'll take it, try writing it down. Get her to do the same, swap, turn away from each other and read them. Hopefully you won't end up with a smack in the mouth for your efforts and she'll always have dreamed of dressing up as The Wicked Witch of the West.

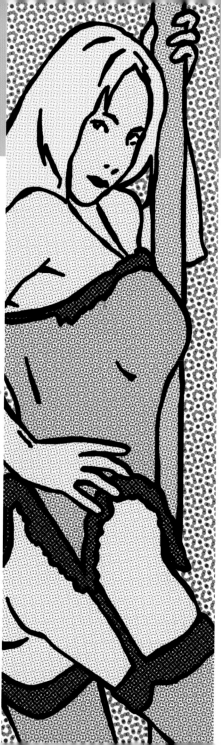

Sex Toys

It's hard to believe it, but sex toys for men have come a long way since the invention of blow-up sheep and dolls. OK, so the sheep were always meant as a joke, but hey, you can't blame a bloke if he's lonely once in a while. As for the dolls, open mouthed, wide eyed inflatable 'ladies' with the required amount of entry ports (mouth, vagina, ears, nostrils... and so on) and nylon pubic hair, you've got to have some imagination to believe that she'll get up and make you breakfast in the morning. One bonus is that they don't nag you or moan about lying in the wet patch. You can also come in her face and it won't sting her eyes, but hey, you'll never get a decent hand job, will you?

World Of Weird

There are hundreds of different sex toys out there, and you might be surprised at how realistic some of them are – and how expensive. You might think, what the heck, if you're already paying for dinner with a real woman, what's the harm in paying fifty quid for a guaranteed shag which won't mind if you go to sleep right afterwards?

■ *Try the Lori Mouth – a natural mouth in beige rubber with red lips and a six inch deep throat.*

■ *Or how about Luscious Lips – a vibrating jelly mouth with supple lips and a detailed tongue. Fancy that! Obviously all women have a vibrating mouth...*

■ *Then there's Jenna's Vagina & Ass – an ultra realistic mould of the one and only porn star Jenna Jameson's vagina and rear end. Her Mum must be so proud...*

So what's in it for you if your partner whips out her vibrator? If it's a 12-inch double-ended dildo – a trip to casualty. If she's got any sense – that's common sense plus a sense of adventure – she'll make sure she doesn't come up with something that will make you feel completely inferior. If she owns a vibrator it doesn't mean she doesn't want to have sex with you anymore (although perhaps you should just check) and can be good fun if you're prepared to join in. Watch her use it on herself, then take control and press it gently to her neck, nipples, inner thighs and anus, before taking over with the real thing. She can also use it on you. Don't worry, that doesn't mean up your backside, more that she can hold it against your balls for a nice tingling sensation, or tickle your bum with it if you're happy with that. It doesn't mean you're gay, it just means you appreciate a couple of AA batteries in the right place at the right time.

As for specifically designed male sex toys, just take a peek on the internet (though it's advisable not to do it in your lunch hour at work, perhaps at home would be better) and you'll find a whole range of weird and wonderful accessories that can be packed up in nice plain boxes and delivered to your door by an unsuspecting postman thus avoiding any embarassing scenes caused by dropping your shopping on the way home.

▶▶▶ 'Were kisses all the joys in bed, one woman would another wed'

William Shakespeare

In other words, the most famous poet of all time knew that sometimes it's a good idea to bring new pleasures into the bedroom. Except that he put it better than that.

Cock rings fit around the base of your willy and help to retain your erection. They increase sensitivity for you and if you get one with a clit-tickling attachment, you'll both be happy. Anal beads, that sound rather like a sexually transmitted disease - ('Doctor, I think I've got anal beads') are a bit hardcore but can be fun. They get pushed up your bum with a little thread left for your partner to yank on just as you're about to come. Lubrication is a must if want a smooth ride!

Orgasms Explained

Aaah, the orgasm. It's as sweet as scoring the winning goal in the Cup Final, or, at least, sitting on the substitute's bench. As you men seem endlessly fascinated by mechanical things such as car engines, we thought it was time your learned a little more about your own engine and how it works during sex. Armed with this know-how you'll be able to explain to your partner why men always roll over and go to sleep afterwards. She might even start to believe you when you say, 'I can't help it, I'm tired and....zzzzzz'.

Orgasms happen in four stages:

1 Arousal

Your brain knows that having a proper snog or getting your earlobes nibbled is a good thing. This triggers the initial excitement and gives you a hard on. It can also happen, of course, at totally inappropriate moments, such as on the beach, in church or at your in-laws during Sunday lunch. Just don't move on to stage two under these circumstances.

2 Plateau

As things get going, your heart rate speeds up and your blood pressure rises – much the same as it would if you were watching a wet t-shirt contest. Breathing becomes more rapid and your body temperature starts increasing. It's around this time that you'll be hoping she's feeling the same, or you might have to go and put the coffee on instead.

A man's orgasm lasts a mere few seconds. A woman's lasts a bit longer, and if she's lucky (or watching a film with Johnny Depp in it) even a few minutes. However, king of the orgasm is the humble pig, whose sexual ecstacy lasts a whopping 30 minutes. Who said men are pigs? If only!

3 Orgasm

Stage three only happens if you've both successfully passed through stages one and two. In other words, not every woman will have an orgasm, but it's your job to try and help her to do so. If she's fallen asleep or is on the phone to her Mum, you're doing something wrong. Either go back to the start of this book, or resign yourself to spending the evening flicking through your back copies of motor magazines. If things are going well, however, your major and minor muscles will begin to contract, nerve endings will send waves of contractions through the pelvic floor muscles and you might even start to hyperventilate. This is the point of no return, when even if your partner has just left the bed and gone to the super-market, you'll still have to come somewhere. Contractions spread up through the testicles and out through – you got it – your willy.

4 'Zzzzzz'

Blood pressure, heart rate and breathing all go back to normal and the muscle fibres in the penis contract, pushing blood away so that your willy deflates like a burst balloon. This all happens within the space of a few minutes in a guy, but if you haven't come, you'll end up with a dragging feeling in your balls that can be pretty uncomfortable. You'll also probably be really hacked off, which is why even if she has lost interest for the time being, you should finish yourself off. It's for your own good, honestly. In women this all takes a bit longer (not the willy bit – we're talking the labia and nipples). This is when she'll start asking you what you're thinking, whether you should get married or not and if you think she's got a fat bum. Luckily, thanks to science, you'll already be asleep. Bingo!

Playing It Safe

If you're the type of man who would say any of the following: 'I hate condoms, I can't feel anything when I'm inside you', 'I haven't got one, let's just do it anyway', or 'I'm not wearing that!' as if your partner had just asked you to dress up in your granny's nightie, you definitely need to carry on reading this section.

Condoms are still the best bet for avoiding sexually transmitted diseases, unwanted babies and wet patches, although it seems as though it's always the woman who ends up sleeping in it anyway. Add a spermicidal lubricant or use condoms containing

Top Tip: Perfect the art of going down on a woman and putting on a condom at the same time. Keep the condom nearby, get busy on your partner, and when she's in a state of ecstasy, keep your face between her legs, unwrap the condom and slip it on. As you come up for air she should be more than ready for penetrative sex and hey presto, you're already sorted. It avoids that fumbling and passion-killing 'Where is it? I think you've put your cup of tea on top of it and now it's melted!' moment.

spermicide and you'll be better protected than Fort Knox – unless you're allergic to spermicide, in which case you'll probably feel as though you've been wearing a condom dusted with chilli powder.

Male condoms only carry around a 2% failure rate, although if you're partner isn't well lubricated (and that's your job, sunshine) or the condom itself is not lubricated during sex, it can burst due to the friction, and no, it's not because you're 'so big'. Just make sure you use a lubricant specifically designed for use with condoms rather than baby oil. Oil-based products can dissolve rubber, and that's the last thing you'd want.

Always check the expiry date on condoms and if your partner has long nails, or raggedy, chewed ones, open the packet yourself to avoid the risk of making a tear in it. When you have finished having sex, make absolutely sure that either you or your partner firmly holds on to the condom at the base of your willy before you withdraw; staying inside her until your erection deflates might cause the sperm to leak from the condom.

We've Heard It All Before

Men are champions when it comes to excuses, particularly when it comes to why they 'can't' wear a condom. No, you are not 'too big'. You all know that condoms blow up to the size of balloons and hold about three pints of water before bursting, so unless you're the world's most amazing undiscovered porn star you'll be fine. If condoms irritate you – and that's not just because you don't like them – then switch to a latex-free brand. And for the record, any woman whom you've just met who is happy to let you go without should raise your suspicions, not your erection. After all, you've no idea who's been there before you... unless the postman, the milkman and the man from the gas board are all still in the lounge comparing notes.

There are so many different types of condom available that you really can't complain that there isn't one to suit you. Well, you can, but it won't do any good. Ribbed or dotted condoms can increase friction, but need a good lubricant. If you think you're allergic to latex, try polyurethane condoms and apply your favourite lubricant, whether oil-based or not. Flavoured condoms can actually be quite pleasant for your partner and not just during oral sex (mmm, strawberry flavoured willy!) as they leave a nice fruity smell wafting around the room.

If you don't hold onto the condom when you withdraw and it gets lost inside your girlfriend or if it bursts, or if you have a lapse of common sense and don't use one at all, be a gent and accompany your partner to the chemist for the morning after pill. It's available without prescription in most countries and should be taken within 72 hours of sex. If you find any sores, blisters, itchiness or swelling in the genital area, then you could have contracted an STD, so go to your doctor or the clinic right away. It goes without saying that if you have picked something up, you must not have sex until you've been checked out. A yearly check-up will keep your sexual health on the right track. Just make an appointment, take your trousers down, close your eyes and think of better things, and hopefully all will be well.

After all, what's five minutes in a cold doctor's surgery with your pants down, if it means getting the all-clear for say, 10 minutes in a warm bedroom with, you guessed it, those pants down again?

love in the dark

For Him

NOTE: For the best luminous results, expose the illustrations on the following pages to light for a couple of minutes before switching the light off